The radio mystery

Tessa Krailing

Nelson

Contents

Kevin's radio

One Monday morning, Kevin brought a radio to school.
It was small and square and black and
it wasn't his own radio.
It was his brother Rick's radio.
Rick would be cross when he found out because
he had not said Kevin could take it.

Tessa saw the radio and shouted,
'Look, everyone! Kevin has got a radio.'
All the kids came to look at the radio.
They all wanted to know about it.
'Where did you get it, Kevin?' asked Rocky.
'Yes, where did you get it?' asked Jamila.
'It's my brother's,' said Kevin.
'Did he say you could have it?' asked Ben.
'Yes,' said Kevin.

Kevin took the radio into the classroom.
It was playing his favourite record and
he sang along with it.
Mr Belter looked up.
'What's that terrible noise?' he asked.
'It sounds like a frightened cat!'
Mr Belter went over to Kevin.
The other kids laughed.

6

'Kevin!' shouted Mr Belter.

Kevin jumped and switched off the radio.

'No radios in school,' said Mr Belter.

'You know that, Kevin.

Give the radio to me.

I shall put it away in my drawer.'

The other kids laughed, but Kevin wasn't very pleased.

7

Kevin was worried.
He had to take that radio back before
Rick found out that it was missing.
If he went home without it, what could he
tell his brother?
He knew Rick would be very cross.
He saw Mr Belter put it in the drawer.
'What am I going to do?' Kevin thought.

School was over for the day.
Kevin went to Mr Belter.
'Please could I have my radio back?' he asked.
'No,' said Mr Belter.
'You can have it back at the end of the week.
Then you will remember about
no radios in school.
Now run along home, Kevin.'
So Kevin had to go without the radio.

Rocky and Ben were going home when
they saw Kevin.
'Aren't you going home?' asked Ben.
'Not yet,' said Kevin.
He did not want to go home without
Rick's radio.
He had to get it back.
He waited for Mr Belter to go home.

As soon as it was dark, Kevin went
back to school.
He looked around.
There was no-one about.
He went over to the classroom window and
looked in.

Kevin was just about to open the window when
a light came on in the classroom.
He was surprised and he moved back quickly.
He saw that the window was broken.
Someone had broken into the school!

The burglar

Kevin looked through the window.
He could see someone with a torch at
Mr Belter's table.
What was he doing?
'This is just like TV,' thought Kevin.
'He must be a burglar.
Wow! A burglar in Waterloo School!'

Kevin kept very still, looking through
the window all the time.
He would have to wait for
the burglar to go before he could get
his radio back.
'How long is he going to be?' thought Kevin.
'I have to get home.
Rick will see that his radio is missing and
Dad will see that I am missing!'
Then Kevin saw the burglar opening
Mr Belter's drawer.
'Wow!' thought Kevin again.
'This is better than TV!'

The burglar took Mr Belter's cash-box
out of the drawer, and
something small and square and black.
'Oh, no!' thought Kevin.
The burglar was stealing Rick's radio!
Kevin was very worried.
He had to do something.
He had to get the radio back.

Suddenly, the burglar looked up and saw Kevin.
He ran to the window and opened it.
He grabbed the radio in one hand and
the cash-box in the other.
He jumped through the window and pushed Kevin
out of the way.

But Kevin moved quickly.
'Stop!' he shouted.
'Give me back my radio!'
Kevin grabbed the burglar's arm.
The man was surprised.
He dropped the radio and ran off.

Kevin looked around for the radio.
When he found it he picked it up.
He was worried.
It might be broken.
He switched it on and was very pleased
because it was OK.
Kevin ran home quickly.
He had to put the radio back before Rick
found out that it was missing.
And he had to get back before his Dad got
too worried and started looking for him.

Who was the burglar?

Next day Mr Belter came into the classroom
followed by a policeman.
'I have to talk to you all about something
important,' he said.
'Last night the school was broken into.
A burglar took Kevin's radio and my cash-box.
Now PC Kent wants to talk to you.'

PC Kent looked at the children.
'Did anyone see anything strange last night?'
he asked them.
The children said nothing, but Kevin looked worried.
'If you remember anything strange you must
tell Mr Belter,' said the policeman before
he left the classroom.

21

At break-time, the kids went outside.

'Remember last night?' Rocky said to Ben.

'We saw Kevin outside the school.

I think Kevin was the burglar.'

'Yes,' said Ben. 'He wanted his radio back and
he took the cash-box too.'

Rocky and Ben did not talk to Kevin.

'They think I did it,' thought Kevin.

'They think I was the burglar.

But if I tell them what I saw,

no-one will believe me.'

Kevin was glad when school was over for the day.

But when Kevin got home, PC Kent was there.
'Now then,' said the policeman.
'Do you know anything about this radio of yours?'
Kevin told him all about the burglar.
'Will I go to prison?' Kevin asked.
'Not if what you have told me is true,' said PC Kent.
'But first we have to catch this man.
You must tell me what he looked like.'
Kevin told PC Kent what he could remember
about the man.

The policeman left to look for the burglar.
Kevin was still very unhappy.
He wasn't sure that PC Kent believed him.
Suddenly, he knew what to do!
He would find the burglar, and then
people would believe him.
Kevin went out to look for the burglar.

Got him red-handed!

Four days later, Kevin was going down the
High Street.
It was full of people doing their Saturday shopping.
Suddenly he saw someone he remembered.
'Who is that man?' he thought.
Kevin was sure he had seen him before.
Could it be the burglar?
The man was going quickly down the street.
Kevin started to follow him.
There were so many people that it was difficult.
And Kevin had to be careful.
The man must not know he was being followed.

Kevin followed the man carefully.
Soon they were in a small street.
The man went inside a house.
Was that where he lived?
Kevin had to make sure.
He would look through the window.

He was just about to look in when he saw
PC Kent.
'What do you think you are doing?'
said the policeman.
'The burglar lives here.'I followed him,'
said Kevin. 'I saw him go into this house.'
'Yes, we saw him too,' said PC Kent.
'We know him well!
We have been looking for him for months.
Now you just wait outside.
We will catch him.'

Kevin waited outside the house.
He saw PC Kent and a policewoman open
the door carefully and go inside.
Kevin was worried.
Would they catch the burglar or
would he get away?
If they didn't get him, people would still
think Kevin had taken the radio and
the cash-box.

Suddenly, the door opened.
The burglar ran out, but PC Kent and
the policewoman were too quick for him.
They grabbed him.
'Got you red-handed!' said PC Kent.
'Look, here is the cash-box!
Let's take it back to Mr Belter.'

On Monday PC Kent came into
the classroom again.
He told the children that they had got
the burglar.
'He is in prison now,' he said.
'Mr Belter has got his cash-box, and
Kevin has his radio.'
He smiled at Kevin.
Rocky and Ben did not look too happy.
They had thought the burglar was Kevin and
they had told the others it was Kevin.
How could they say they were sorry?

31

Rocky and Ben went over to Kevin.
'Want to play with us, Kevin?' asked Rocky.
'Want some of my crisps?' said Ben.
'OK,' said Kevin, and he took a crisp.
He was pleased.
He had got Rick's radio back, and Rocky and
Ben were sorry and wanted to be friends.